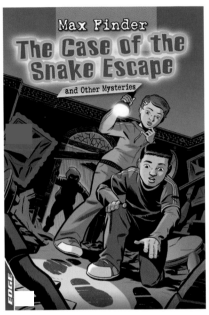

978 1 4451 0603 8

978 1 4451 0604 5

978 1 4451 0605 2

978 1 4451 0606 9

Max Finder

The Case of the Movie Set Mischief

and Other Mysteries

This edition first published in 2011 by
Franklin Watts
338 Euston Road
London NW1 3BH

Franklin Watts Australia
Level 17/207 Kent Street
Sydney NSW 2000

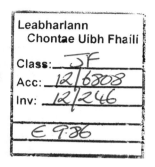

Paperback original

First published in Canada by Owlkids Books Inc.
Puzzle text: Maria Birmingham
Puzzle illustrations: John Lightfoot
Comic colouring: Peter Dawes (p. 23, 29, 41, 57, 63, 69); Chris Stone (p. 11, 17, 35, 49)
Series Design: John Lightfoot/Lightfoot Art & Design Inc.
UK edition designers: Jonathan Hair and Anna-Marie D'Cruz

A CIP catalogue record for this book is available from the British Library

ISBN: 978 1 4451 0605 2
Dewey classification: 741.5'971

Printed in China

Franklin Watts is a division of Hachette Children's Books,
an Hachette UK company.

www.hachette.co.uk

Max Finder

The Case of the Movie set Mischief

and Other Mysteries

Liam O'Donnell

Michael Cho

EDGE
FRANKLIN WATTS

LONDON•SYDNEY

Max Finder
The Case of the
Movie Set Mischief
and Other Mysteries

Contents

Cases

Max Finder
The Case of the Movie Set Mischief
and Other Mysteries

Contents

Cases

Extra Stuff

Max Finder

The Case of the Movie Set Mischief

and Other Mysteries

HEY, MYSTERY FANS!
Welcome to the Max Finder Mysteries!
Alison and I are really excited to bring you
ten of the best mysteries to hit our town
of Whispering Meadows.
From the **Back-to-School Sneak** to the
Screaming Screening, each mysterious comic
is crammed with clues, stuffed with suspects,
and riddled with enough red herrings to keep
you guessing until the last panel. We've done all
the legwork, but solving the mystery is up to
you! Read the mysteries, follow the clues and
try to crack the case. All the solutions are at
the back of the book. But remember: real
detectives never peek.
So, fire up your mystery radar and get solving!

Max

P.S. Check out the BONUS puzzles and the
Writer's Notebook, too!

Back-to-School Sneak

Max Finder
MYSTERY

The Case of the Back-to-School Sneak

Did you know the Egyptian pharaohs enjoyed the first magic show over 6,500 years ago? Max Finder here, fact collector and ace detective. It's a new school year and that means new kids, new teachers and a new mystery.

Max, someone took my video-game player from my coat pocket!

None of the other coats were touched. The thief knew where to look.

I'll find your video-game player, Ethan.

Jake Granger is new to our school. He thinks he has psychic powers. But he likes mysteries, so he can't be all bad.

Yesterday Jake found Nanda Kanwar's missing maths book stuffed in the rubbish of the boys' changing room.

I'm picking up strong vibes from behind the shed.

Check it out!

How did he do that?

Go back to your Sherlock Holmes books, Max. There's a new detective in town.

Would <u>You</u> Rather?
Back–To–School Edition

Answer the mind-bending questions below.
Quiz your friends and family, too!

▶ **Would you rather** be the teacher's pet **or** the class clown?

▶ **Would you rather** fly to school with your own jetpack **or** travel through secret underground tunnels?

▶ **Would you rather** have straight A's **or** score the winning goal at the city-wide football tournament?

▶ **Would you rather** take a class trip to the top of Mount Everest **or** to a deserted island in the South Pacific?

▶ **Would you rather** be the school band's star tuba player **or** the spelling competition champion?

▶ **Would you rather** be able to pass invisible notes in class **or** finish your homework in three minutes every day?

▶ **Would you rather** be in the same class as your best friend **or** your favourite teacher?

▶ **Would you rather** get top marks in tests with your photographic memory **or** win track events with your Olympic speed?

▶ **Would you rather** have something new to wear every day **or** something new to eat for lunch every day?

▶ **Would you rather** be the DJ at the school dance **or** take the lead role in the school play?

Haunted Haunted House

The Case of the
Haunted Haunted House

Max Finder
MYSTERY

Did you know that the world's largest lollipop is taller than a giraffe? Max Finder here, fact collector and ace detective. Today is Halloween, and Alison and I are checking out Old Oak Manor.

This empty house is perfect for Jessica Peeves's halloween party. But why are we here so early? You don't believe the ghost stories about this place, do you, Max?

No way. Basher is mad because Jessica didn't invite him. She wants us to see if he's planning any pranks tonight.

You may own Oak Manor now, Mr Peeves, but the spirits that live here won't let you tear it down!

No ghost is going to stop me building a shopping centre on this land, and neither will you, Mr Price!

You'll regret this!

Why is that guy so mad at your dad, Jessica?

That's Victor Price. He thinks Oak Manor is haunted and that knocking it down will unleash a curse on the whole town.

NO TRESPASSING

Jessica took us around the back to start our investigation.

Daddy won't let Basher through the front door, so if he's planning any pranks, he'll be sneaking around here tonight.

Looks like someone has been taking care of the garden.

It's a woman named Hazel. She doesn't have a garden, so she takes care of this one. Daddy told her to stay away, but she keeps coming back.

Look out!

HAZEL!

I don't like children snooping around the garden – especially you, Jessica. Your Daddy will be tearing it up soon enough.

Ghoulish
Gravestones

Jessica's dad set up funny gravestones at the Halloween party.

Can you match the first and last names to come up with the phony full names?

M.T.	Ghost
Dr.	Dead
Ricky D.	Stein
R.U.	Parted
Izzy	Peace
Dee	Tomb
Frank N.	Bones
Ima	Acula
Rustin	Next

ANSWERS ON PAGE 84

Mars Malfunction

Max Finder

MYSTERY

The Case of the Mars Malfunction

Did you know the place on Earth most like Mars is Devon Island in Nunavut, Canada? Max Finder here, ace detective, fact collector and spaceship navigator. We're at the Meadows Science Centre, in the middle of a Space Challenge Competition.

Finder, take your calculations to the mission log room! We're running out of time!

MISSION CONTROL

YEOW!

Don't blow your hyperdrive, Hans. I'm going!

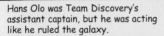

Hans Olo was Team Discovery's assistant captain, but he was acting like he ruled the galaxy.

MISSION CONTROL

Hans does know we're only *pretending* to land on Mars, doesn't he?

Our real captain was Dorothy Pafko. But when we got to the Log Room, the head of the competition, Commander Ripley, was giving the orders.

MISSION LOG ROOM

Dorothy, you're not allowed to go into the other team's control room! One more mistake and you'll be demoted.

But I received a message that I was needed in their control room.

CHALLENGER TEAM   DISCOVERY TEAM

That's a lie. She was spying on my crew!

James was the captain of Team Challenger, the group of kids we were up against in the competition.

James is setting me up. If I'm not captain, he thinks his team will win the competition.

Let's keep an eye on him.

Back at Team Discovery's Control Room, someone had turned off our computers.

MISSION CONTROL

I left to grab Drew Bacca a larger vest from the maintenance room. When I got back, the computers were dead! Team Challenger must have cut our power!

Hans was really mad when he wasn't chosen as captain. Looks like he can't handle the job anyway.

I'll deal with it, Hans. Take the vest to Drew in the research lab and get back here.

Hans was the one who gave Dorothy the message from Team Challenger. We asked him about it on the way to the lab.

Some kid in an orange science centre cap and a yellow vest gave me the message.

RESEARCH LAB

Hey, Drew. I brought you a bigger vest.

Thanks, Hans. Commander Ripley is looking for you. She wants the keys to the maintenance room back.

Let's find this kid in the orange hat.

Outside the Log Room we learned that James and Commander Ripley shared a secret.

James, let's get to work. We don't want Commander Ripley to make Team Discovery the winners.

Don't worry about that. Aunt Shirley says we have a good chance of winning.

MISSION LOG ROOM

Aunt Shirley? He means Ripley!

Across the hall, Ripley wasn't having any luck getting into the Maintenance Room without the keys.

If I don't get into this room, I can't restart your computers.

Down the hall, no one saw us sneak into Team Challenger's Control Room.

I still don't see the kid in the orange hat.

We better get out of here before we're caught.

Nooo!

That's Dorothy! I think the yell came from the log room.

Someone stole our mission log book!

The thief can't be far. Let's go!

There's someone in an orange cap down the hall!

The log book contained all our findings for the space mission. If it went missing, Team Challenger would win the space competition!

AHA!

Drop that hat, James!

SLiiiiDE!!

I didn't take your dumb log book. Some kid ran out of the research lab, stuffed the hat in the bin and then ran past me.

You're lying.

Whatever. I've got to get back to my team. We're about to land on Mars. Face it – you guys have lost!

Did you find the log book?

No. But I have a feeling it's in the research lab.

We searched the room but couldn't find the log book.

It's not here! What are we going to do?

I knew James was lying.

Hey! I've got something and it's heavy.

WRRRRR!

CHUNK!

The log book! You found it, Drew!

And I know who put it there.

Do you know who is trying to mess with the Mars mission? All the clues are here. Turn to page 77 for the solution.

KEYBOARD Code

Commander Ripley has given Max and his team another challenge.
Grab your notepad and decode her mysterious message.

Hint: Replace each letter with one that's either
to the left or the right of it on the keyboard.

Ywsn Sodxpbreu:

Tpi ksbfwf im Nstd!

Qst yi fp!

Vpnnsbfwt Eookru

ANSWER ON PAGE 84

Ice Village Vandal

Max Finder

The Case of the Ice Village Vandal

Did you know that a snowy owl needs to eat twelve mice a day to be healthy? Max Finder here, fact collector and ace detective. In case you missed the giant elf, the Christmas holidays have arrived.

The Ice Village opens tomorrow! We can go skating!

Your detective skills always amaze me, Alison.

ICE VILLAGE OPENS TOMORROW

HOT CHOCOLATE

CREAK!

Okay, Sherlock! Let's find out what time the ice skating starts.

CREAK!

HOT CHOCOLATE

CREAK!

Listen to that elf, Zack! It creaks all day long. It's driving me totally bonkers!

I know, Lindsey. But the floodlights on it light up the rink. No waving elf, no night-time ice skating.

I can't stand it! I guess all this noise means you can't take your naps anymore.

Naps? I should be so lucky. There's no way I can get any sleep during work.

Alison headed home to sharpen her skates, but I had one more stop to make.

DINGG!

Huh?

Hi, Mr Kroft. My mum dropped off some boots here for repairs.

The boots aren't ready yet, Max. I'm so tired I can't get any work done.

I live above this shop and the elf lights are so bright I can't sleep. Mr Dumont, the golf course owner, insists on keeping them on all night!

The next evening, when I arrived at the Ice Village, the elf statue wasn't on. Mr Dumont was not happy.

Out of my way, Zack. Let's get this thing fixed quickly.

The circuit board is gone, Mr Dumont. It has to be ordered and could takes weeks to arrive.

Someone pulled out the elf's circuit board, Max! Without the lights, we can't skate.

ZACK!!! What have you been doing?!

Zack, you've been napping in here! Find that circuit board or you're fired!

The thief used keys to open the lock. Who had keys to the elf statue?

Just me, Mr Dumont and Zack, if he hasn't lost them. He's always getting new ones cut.

The next day, we ran into Becca. She was working with the animal shelter to get the sign's moving arm turned off for good. The noise was scaring away snowy owls.

I'm glad the circuit board was taken. If we can prove snowy owls live on the golf course, Mr Dumont will have to keep that sign turned off.

See you guys later!

She had a reason to steal the circuit board. Let's keep an eye on her.

I'll show you where it is, Becca. But hurry up, before Mr Dumont sees us.

I bet Zack is going to show Becca where he hid the circuit board!

Let's hitch a ride.

VROOM!

TRIP!

Oops!

I missed my ride but caught a clue instead.

Interesting.

Meanwhile, Alison was making discoveries of her own.

Why are we all the way out here, Zack?

Check it out!

This is exactly what we've been looking for!

Whatever these are, they're important.

When Zack and Becca returned, the fireworks really started.

Zack! I found this in the clubhouse. Only you, Lindsey and I have keys to get in there. Lindsey isn't here today, so that leaves you.

Want your circuit board back? Turn off the sign at night!

I know who wrote that note.

And I know who is sabotaging the skating rink!

Do you know who took the elf's circuit board? All the clues are here. Turn to page 78 for the solution.

⊙ Places Everyone

Max and Alison play ice hockey on Saturdays with their friends.

Figure out which kid played in each position on Max's team.

Players:
Max, Alison, Basher, Jessica, Ethan and Becca.

Clues:
1. The goalie was a girl.

2. Both kids who played defense were boys.

3. Becca played to the right of Jessica.

4. Basher was left wing.

5. Max played directly behind Becca.

Cast-off Costume

Max Finder
MYSTERY

The Case of the
Cast-off Costume

Did you know the woodland frog can survive being frozen solid? Max Finder here, fact collector and ace detective. Snowy Sundays mean tobogganing here in Whispering Meadows, and Alison steering means a crash is near.

Hold on, Max! This is going to be a fast ride.

Speed is great, Alison, but control is better. Watch out for that...

BUMP!

We crashed into a soft snow drift and landed in a new mystery.

This is the grouch costume for the school show tomorrow night.

The school isn't far away. Someone must have dumped the costume here.

The show is called "How the Grouch Hated Christmas". The grouch is a mean creature trying to ruin the holidays. Courtney LeGuin has spent weeks making the grouch costume.

Why would anyone ruin Basher's costume?

Yup, Basher is the grouch.

Basher! This is Basher's costume?

Basher McGintley is a big bully and king of the grouches. Courtney said Basher's parents forced him to be in the show, but once he started, he really enjoyed it.

Basher likes something that doesn't involve punching? Weird.

He likes acting but hates the grouch costume. He says it makes him look like a dork.

Courtney had hung up the costume and said goodbye to Jessica Peeves at the end of yesterday's rehearsal.

I'm the best at sewing, so Jessica is making costumes for the grouch's gang. She always leaves rehearsals last.

We took the costume to our forensic expert, Zoe Palgrave. Zoe loves the science of mysteries and has the lab in her cellar to prove it.

FINGERPRINT CHART

The size and shape of the hole tell me it was made with a fist. And... what's this?

Looks like wool. Or it could be thread from the grouch's costume.

Let's put it under the microscope and find out.

It was wool, but not the expensive kind called angora. It was regular wool used to make the winter hats and gloves worn by nearly every kid at school. It wasn't much, but it was our first clue.

Courtney said Basher's friends, Dwayne and Shayne, teased him about his acting, and Basher was sick of it. The next day, Basher was his usual charming self.

Eat yellow snow, you two. Jeff Coleman ruined my costume. That twerp wanted to be the grouch, but he was too small.

In the show, Jeff was playing one of the grouch's gang, but we found him playing hide-from-the-bully.

Don't tell Basher I'm here! I bet Jessica ruined the costume to get back at Courtney for bragging about being the best costume maker.

After school, we checked behind the gym for clues. Instead we found Basher. Dwayne and Shayne had found him, too.

Hey, Basher! Put your grouch mask on. Your real face is too scary!

Keep it up, Dwayne, and I'll knock you back to Year One!

NO HANDBALL NO SKATEBOARDING

EXIT ONLY

Let's get out of here.

EXIT ONLY

What's Basher doing with this hat from the show?

EXIT ONLY

Looks like it was wedged under the costume room door. The hat is covered in grease. That's how the mystery person got in.

henchman #3 Jeff Coleman

Jeff has some explaining to do.

The show started in an hour. Jessica Peeves told us Jeff had complained about not getting the part as the grouch. She wasn't impressed with his dirty hat.

HOLIDAY PAGEANT TONIGHT

CAST & CREW ENTRANCE

If I get grease on my new angora mittens, I'll kill that little slob.

Mrs Janssen, the show director, said last week Basher asked to wear his jeans on stage instead of the grouch costume.

I told him no. But the show must go on, and a grouch in jeans is better than no grouch at all!

With the show starting very soon, the costume room was in chaos.

CAST ONLY

Basher, I didn't ruin your costume, honest!

For the last time, I don't need your help, Jessica.

This show has gone on long enough. I know who ruined the grouch costume.

Do you know who wrecked the grouch costume? All the clues are here. Turn to page 78 for the solution.

What Kind of Detective Would You Be?

Take this quiz and see where you might belong in the world of detectives.
Write your answers in a notebook.

1. **Your sister's diary has gone missing and she asks for help. You:**
   a. interview everyone in the house to get some clues
   b. search her bedroom for evidence
   c. put the diary back before she catches you with it

2. **You would describe yourself as:**
   a. mischievous
   b. born with an eye for detail
   c. suspicious

3. **A famous painting was stolen from a museum. If you had been first on the scene, you would have:**
   a. asked to examine the museum security camera recordings
   b. collected fingerprints and other clues from the museum
   c. left it up to the police to solve

4. **If you were a member of a crime team like the ones on TV's C.S.I. you'd prefer to be:**
   a. the detective who interviews the suspects
   b. the crime scene investigator
   c. the police officer who secures the scene

5. **Your best friend says someone has been rummaging through his locker. You:**
   a. secretly try to solve the mystery on your own
   b. offer to help your friend search for clues
   c. tell your friend it's no big deal since nothing's missing

6. **If you were following a suspect, you'd:**
   a. keep a safe distance so you weren't detected
   b. try to gather evidence the suspect was leaving behind
   c. call for back-up

RATINGS PAGE 84

Slime Tank Sabotage

Max Finder
MYSTERY

The Case of the Slime Tank Sabotage

Did you know that banana slugs use their slime trails to find mates? Max Finder here, fact collector and ace detective, dangling on the edge of a slime-tank disaster.

Okay, Alison. It's all up to you. Answer my question correctly or your friend Max Finder takes a dive in the slime tank!

Are you okay? Did you see what happened, Zoe?

No! We were too busy running from the avalanche of slime.

The tank wasn't the only thing that was bursting. Bull O'Wiley is a bigwig at the TV station. He was unloading his own tank of slime onto the show's producer, my mum.

I told you that tank wasn't safe! Get this mess cleaned up and get your show out of here – you're cancelled!

That tank was reinforced with metal. Someone sabotaged it to ruin the show.

I just got to the studio and heard what happened! That sucks!

I thought you'd be happy, Johnny. With my show cancelled, we won't have to share the studio anymore.

Hey! That's Johnny Vile, the host of *Punk My Bike*.

Punk my what?

They take a kid's bike and turn it into a two-wheeled hot rod. Johnny moves the set out of the way when we shoot the quiz show.

Hey, guys! Check this out!

Zoe was our forensics expert. She could find clues in a sea of slime.

The bolts are missing their tops. That's why the tank burst.

If we can prove the tank was sabotaged, maybe Mr O'Wiley won't cancel the show.

Backstage, Zoe used Dr Disaster's tools to get a closer look at the metal bar.

Just as I thought. Look at this.

Under the magnifying glass, it was clear that the bolts holding the tank together had been cut with a saw. We needed to find the person who did the cutting.

Zoe had to go home, but Alison and I stuck around the studio. Good thing we did because the real show was just starting.

The woman charging past is Maureen. She plays Igora on the quiz show. She was arguing with Carl, the actor playing Dr Disaster.

STOMP! STOMP! STOMP!

You'd like to pin it on me so I get fired. The slime tank was your idea, Carl. I told you it was dangerous.

Are you accusing me of tampering with that tank? I saw YOU messing with it before the show. You caused it to break to make me look bad!

Carl admitted that the slime tank was his idea. But he blamed Maureen for the accident.

She's jealous because she isn't Dr Disaster. She sabotaged the tank to get me fired. Ask her yourself. I bet she's backstage. She goes there to sulk.

Now go away. I have to call my agent.

The slime tank has been a real pain. This morning, Johnny Vile was nosing around it. Then I caught some kid messing with it before the show.

Some of the studio audience were still hanging around asking questions about the slime tank disaster. We were interviewing the security guard when I overheard Basher McGintley, bragging that he had all the answers.

7 CKWM

I know why the slime tank burst, but there's no way I'm telling anyone.

Let's get out of here.

Basher wasn't on our science quiz team. He only showed up today to laugh at us if we lost.

The tops of the bolts!

Snooping in my rubbish, Finder?

WAAALP!

No one knows about those bits of metal. I found them around the slime tank. Don't make trouble for me or I'll slime your head.

We still needed to talk to Maureen, the actor who plays Igora on the quiz show. It was dark backstage. Perfect for sulking. And perfect for plotting a crime.

Hello, little detectives . . . looking for me?

Maureen!

Maureen told us that Carl had been offered a Hollywood movie role. But he couldn't break his quiz-show contract, so he was stuck playing Dr Disaster.

With the quiz show cancelled, Carl is free to be in the movie and become a big star.

In the corner was the set for *Punk My Bike*. Once a week, Johnny Vile took the set apart to make room for the quiz show.

Impressive, isn't it? I've been here since this morning putting this set together for tonight's show.

That bike has a DVD player! I wonder if it comes with a remote.

Johnny Vile didn't have much time to talk, but he did have a theory about the slime tank.

This TV studio has more gossip than a soap opera!

That gossip has helped me solve the mystery. I know who sabotaged the slime tank.

That's a lot of tools just to fix a bike.

That friend of yours, Basher, is the one who cut the bolts on the tank. I saw him messing with it before the show.

Do you know who sent the slime sliding? Turn to page 79 for the solution.

Slime Time

Uh-oh. When the slime tank burst, one of Zoe's crime scene files got slimed.

Use your detective skills and see if you can decipher this slimy page.

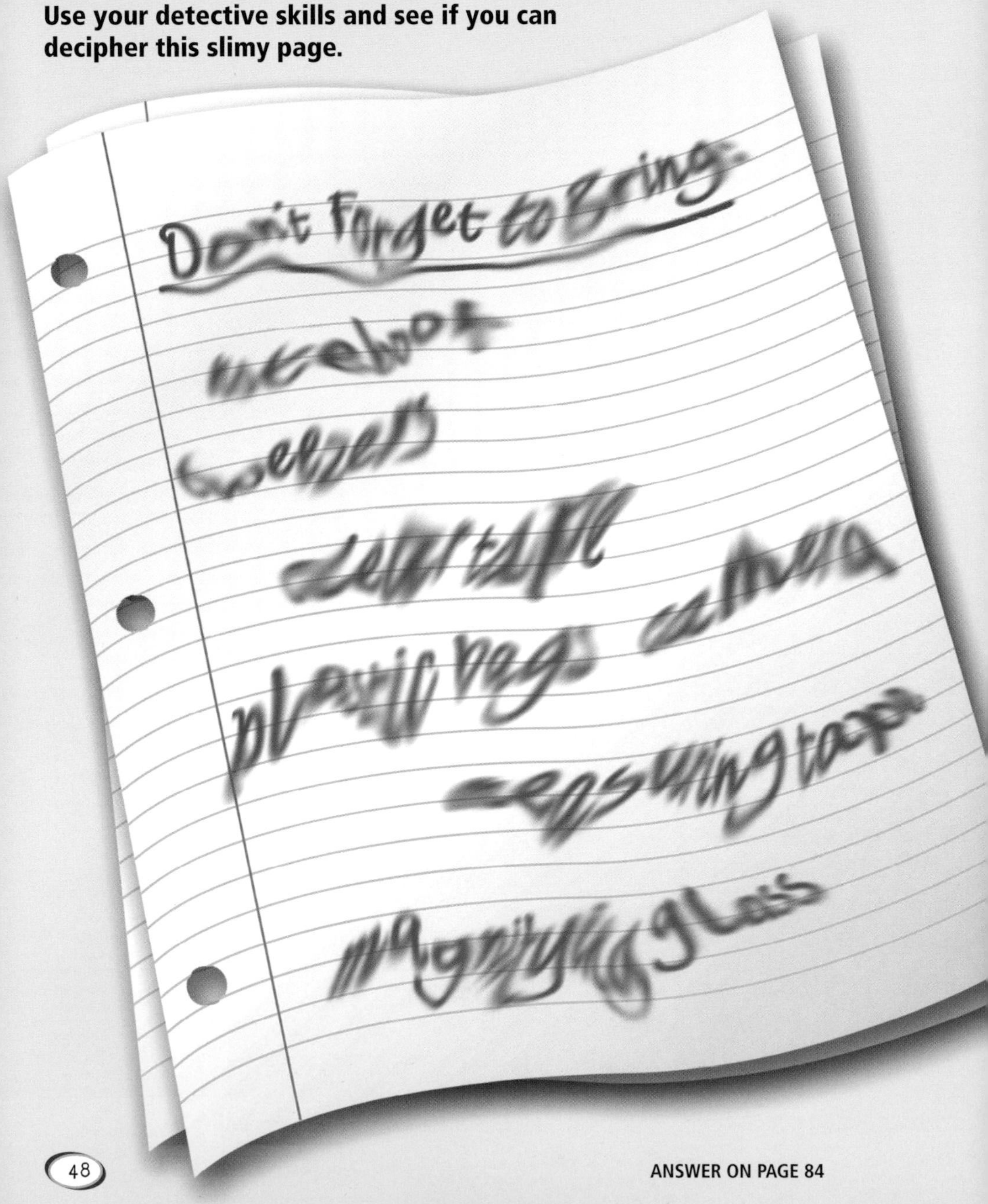

Don't Forget to Bring:

notebook

tweezers

scalpel

plastic bags   camera

measuring tape

magnifying glass

ANSWER ON PAGE 84

Lost Lobster

Max Finder
MYSTERY

The Case of the
Lost Lobster

Hey Max,
Did you know that Capers and Bluenosers are nicknames for people living in Nova Scotia, Canada? Alison Santos here, detective on holiday and cross-Canada traveller. Next stop: Diggers Cove, where we'll spend a few days with my aunt and uncle and my cousins, Patricio and Claudia. Plus I'll get to meet Pato's girlfriend, Katlyn.
See you soon!
Alison

Max Finder
121 Willow Lane
Whispering
Meadows

Welcome to Diggers Cove, Alison!

Want to ditch the parents and get the real tour of the cove?

The harbour was beautiful, but I wasn't impressed with our first stop: the restaurant where Katlyn worked.

That lobster looks so sad, Katlyn.

Lilly, the owner, only cares about attracting tourists. She's afraid Twiggy will climb out of the tank and pinch her.

See you two when you've finished work. We've got to get home for dinner.

The next morning, Claudia and I headed back to the harbour.

Alison! Someone stole Twiggy the lobster!

MAIL

To: sooprsleuth@hypemail.com
From: dtektvgrrl@yeehaw.com
Attached Files: crimescenepics.zip
Re: get that mystery radar working...

Max,
I'm up to my lobster claws in a mystery here. Check out these photos and tell me what you think.

A.

Not much to see....

What happens if I zoom in on the photo?

C·L·I·K

MAIL

To: dtektvgrrl@yeehaw.com
From: sooprsleuth@hypemail.com
Attached Files: fishtankzoom.jpg
Re: mystery radar says...

A,
Check out zoomed photo.
Wish I could be there to help crack the case!

Max

Maybe the thief left a clue.

Stick With It

Max has added the stamp from Alison's postcard to his stamp collection. **Have a look at all of his stamps and see if you can find:**
1. The three identical stamps
2. The stamp that appears upside down and backwards
3. The stamp from New Zealand
4. The stamp with a lighthouse on it
5. The stamp worth 26 pence
6. The stamps featuring birds

ANSWERS ON PAGE 85

Movie Set Mischief

Max Finder
MYSTERY

The Case of the
Movie Set Mischief

This is so cool, Max! I can't believe we're on a real movie set.

Didn't I tell you being my friend would pay off?

Sssh! Quiet on the set, please.

Max Finder here, ace detective and winner of two passes to visit the set of the new blockbuster movie *Dogtown Malone III: Revenge of the Ninja Queen*. It's shooting in Whispering Meadows, and today is the first day of filming.

Places, everybody!

The woman with the curly hair is the director, Petra Jackson. That's Ridge Thorton tied to the stake. He plays Dogtown Malone. The kid beside him is teen superstar Jasmin Newmar.

and...
ACTION!

SNAP!

You can't escape my ninja army, Dogtown Malone.

In this scene you're trying to escape the ninjas. Let's have lots of action, okay?

No worries. Action is my middle name.

The light! It's falling!

Somebody pushed me! I think I sprained my ankle.

What? We have action scenes this afternoon!

Where's Rex?

Over there, Max! It's a ninja.

Hey, you! Stop!

Watch out, kid!

Oh!

Hnf!

Alison, that was amazing!

Are you okay?

Yeah, but the ninja got away.

That's okay. I know who's trying to hurt Jasmin.

And I found her new stunt double! Alison, Do you want to be in my movie?

Do you know who's trying to hurt Jasmin? All the clues are here. Turn to page 81 to find out.

Movie
Mad Lib

On a separate piece of paper, write out and complete the text in the brackets in this Dogtown Malone movie script. Then read it aloud. Have a friend do the same.

Scene 6:
A ninja army has captured Dogtown Malone and Julia. They want the pair to reveal the secret of the lost [vegetable]. The army has locked them in [name of a shop you hate] and left.

Malone
We've got to escape before that army of [clothing item] returns and tries to make us talk. Let's try to ride these [wild animals] and make our way to [planet].

Julia
We'll never make it. We don't have a [type of weapon] or even a [kid's toy]. I told you we should have brought [famous athlete] with us.

Malone
Don't panic. You're starting to sound like a [type of fish] in the middle of [name of a month]. Let's think: what would [name of superhero] do?

Malone hands Julia a [type of tool] from his backpack. But she reaches in her pocket for a [your favourite snack] instead.

Julia
This oughta do the trick. I knew [favourite pet name] would come in handy.

Malone
Hurry, they're coming. Throw me that [something smelly] and we'll race to [name of a country].

Julia
Great idea! They'll never find us there. Unless, of course, the [favourite sports team] are in on this. Then we're sure to end up like [type of junk food].

Max Finder

MYSTERY

The Case of the Hijacked Hat

Inside the airport's VIP lounge, most of the crew had picked up their luggage. But Ridge Thorton, the actor playing Dogtown Malone, and Ryan, the production assistant, weren't having a happy landing.

Where's my Dogtown hat, Ryan? You were in charge of our luggage and now it's gone!

It must be somewhere. Don't worry, we have plenty of other hats you can wear on set tomorrow.

That was my lucky hat! If you don't find it, I'm not finishing this movie.

Petra Jackson, the movie's director, told us that Ridge was very superstitious. On the last Dogtown movie, he refused to go on set because his horoscope predicted bad luck.

We had to stop shooting for a week. It was a disaster. We must find that hat or this movie is doomed!

It was in the cargo hold during the flight, so it must have been taken after the plane landed.

That hat is as famous as Dogtown. You could sell it for a lot of money online. I'll tell security it's been stolen.

If he's right, we'd better find that hat before the thief finds a buyer.

CLICK!

Why is that cleaner taking our photo?

AIRPORT STAFF

Not again!

Chain Reaction

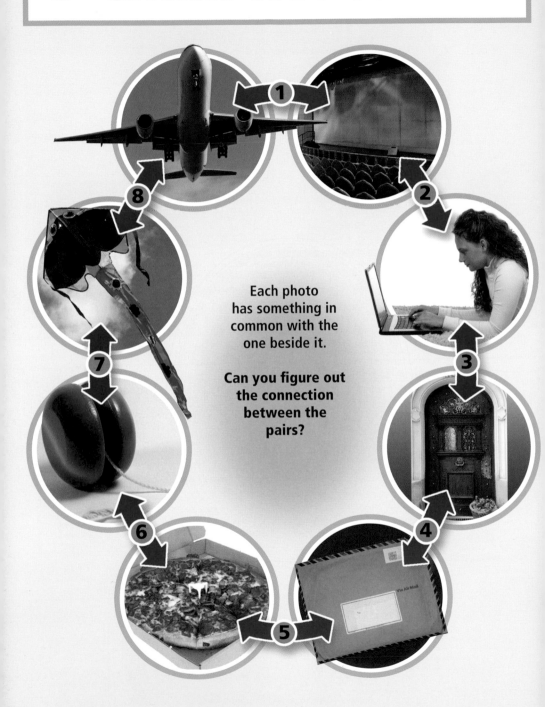

Each photo has something in common with the one beside it.

Can you figure out the connection between the pairs?

ANSWER ON PAGE 85

Screaming Screening

Max Finder MYSTERY

The Case of the Screaming Screening

Being a detective can get you into some cool places, like the back of a limo with teen movie star Jasmin Newmar and her boyfriend, Ashton Cruz. Max Finder, ace detective, here. Alison and I have been helping the crew of the latest *Dogtown Malone* movie, and tonight is the premiere.

Thanks for letting us hitch a ride to the screening, Jasmin.

Are you kidding? Your detective skills saved the movie twice!

Can you lend me some money? I'm totally broke.

Again? I lent you money last week, Ashton.

WORLD PREMIERE
DOGTOWN MALONE III
REVENGE OF THE NINJA QUEEN

Ashton wasn't a big star, but he was trying. He spent most of the limo ride telling me his life story and complaining about how expensive acting lessons are.

Jasmin! Over here, Jasmin!

Jasmin, I love your necklace!

Inside the cinema, we ran into Petra Jackson, the director of the movie, and Ridge Thorton, the actor who plays Dogtown Malone.

Didn't think you two would make it through all those reporters.

Thank you. It's from Louis Regeau, a French designer. He let me wear it tonight.

They're too busy gushing over Jasmin to notice us.

They're really gushing over that necklace. Those jewels could pay for my next movie!

A little later we ran into some celebrities who weren't so happy to see Jasmin doing well.

Did you see Jasmin's necklace? Louis asked me to wear it but then gave it to her instead. She needs to be taught a lesson.

Max, where's Jasmin? The movie is about to start.

Is it me, or is that weird?

He says he went to hairdressing school before he started acting.

Jasmin and Ashton appeared seconds before the movie was about to begin.

Hurry! Petra has started her opening speech already.

Ashton took her to the women's toilet to fix her hair.

We found our seats in time to catch the end of Petra's speech. As the director left the stage, the lights dimmed, but Jasmin had one last live performance to give. . .

AAAAAH!

My necklace! It's been stolen!

Back in the lobby we tried to figure out what happened.

When the lights went out, I felt my neck and my necklace was gone!

Sorry, Ma'am. No one is allowed to leave the cinema while we search it.

What? I will not tolerate this. Let me pass.

Anabella Jockey was in the first Dogtown movie, but they said she was too old for the new one. She's totally jealous of Jasmin.

The police have cleared the cinema to look for it. Hopefully they'll find something. Let's split up and look for clues.

And Jasmin's necklace. Anabella was sitting behind Jasmin in the cinema. I wonder why she wants to leave so badly?

Alison checked out the women's toilet.

Hey! Could this be the clasp from Jasmin's necklace?

Upstairs, Petra was on the phone to her agent and it seemed her money troubles were over.

Things have gone very well here, Frank. I think we'll have no trouble getting the money for our next movie.

Detective! We've got something.

We found these on the floor behind Jasmin's seat.

How did those scissors get past our security?

EVIDENCE

The thief must have used the scissors to cut the necklace from Jasmin's neck.

And I know who did it. The award for worst jewel thief goes to...

Do you know who took Jasmin's necklace? All the clues are here. Turn to page 82 for the solution.

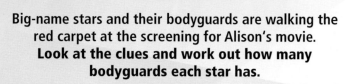

Big-name stars and their bodyguards are walking the red carpet at the screening for Alison's movie. **Look at the clues and work out how many bodyguards each star has.**

Hint:
The stars are
Tad Smit,
Jasmin Newmar,
Petra Jackson,
Ridge Thorton,
Anabella Jockey
and Ashton Cruz.

Clues:

1. There are twenty-six bodyguards on the red carpet.

2. One star has just one bodyguard.

3. Anabella has four bodyguards.

4. Tad has twice as many as Petra.

5. Ridge and Jasmin have the same number of bodyguards.

6. Petra has one more bodyguard than Anabella.

ANSWERS ON PAGE 85

Who? What? When? Where? How? Why?

Who? What? When?

The Case of the Back–to–School Sneak

(page 11)

Who is stealing stuff at school?
• **Jake Granger**. Jake wanted everyone to think he was a great detective, so he took things, hid them and then pretended to find them.

How did Max solve the case?
• Jake worked hard to put the blame on somebody else. But Basher couldn't have been climbing on the garden shed because he was kept inside at the time. Jake wore Basher's jacket.
• Jake cut the leather fibres from Basher's jacket. He planted them at Leslie's desk to put suspicion on the bully.
• Taking someone's watch is a classic magic trick. Jake took Leslie's watch when he was doing the "pull a coin from the ear" trick.
• Jake put Leslie's watch in jelly to make it look like one of Kyle's practical jokes. Max overheard Kyle give Jake the idea.

Conclusion
The detectives confronted Jake with the evidence in private. Jake admitted to the thefts and apologised to the class. At first the kids were mad, but after fixing Basher's jacket and doing a few magic tricks, Jake was one of the gang again.

The Case of the Haunted House

(page 17)

Who or what is haunting Old Oak Manor?
• **Hazel.** She loved the garden so much that she made it look like the house was really haunted to scare Mr Peeves and stop him tearing it down.

How did Max solve the case?
• Hazel used old soup cans for plant pots. They were the same cans used to make noise in the house.
• When she scared Max and Alison in the garden, Hazel had string stuffed into her coat pockets. The same string was used to tie the soup cans together.
• The rope leading out of the attic window was how Hazel escaped. She had used the rope to sneak behind Max, Alison and Jessica.
• Basher had already fled from the house when Max and Alison heard the eerie voice for the second time. Although he had been sneaking around the house, Basher couldn't have been the haunter.

Conclusion
Hazel was found hiding in the bushes behind the manor and admitted to making the house seem haunted.

Case Solutions

With the haunting mystery solved, the actors went to work just as the first party guests arrived. Hazel even used her haunting tools in the attic to make it the best haunted-house party that anyone could remember.

The Case of the Mars Malfunction

(page 23)

Who is sabotaging the space mission?
• **Hans Olo.** Hans was angry at not being picked as captain. First, he tried to get Dorothy in trouble so he could be made captain. When that didn't work, Hans tried to ruin the whole mission.

How did Max solve the case?
• Max and Alison couldn't find the kid who delivered the fake message because he didn't exist. Hans made him up to get Dorothy in trouble.
• Hans had the keys to the Maintenance Room. That meant he could have cut the power to the computers.
• Hans took a yellow vest and an orange hat from the Maintenance Room when he was getting the vest for Drew. He wore them when he stole the log book.
• When Hans arrived at the Research Lab, he had his green vest on backwards because he had got changed so quickly.

Conclusion
Hans admitted to stealing the log book. He hid the book in the sludge and dumped the vest and hat in the rubbish bin just before Max and Alison arrived. Commander Ripley pulled Hans off Team Discovery. Both teams landed on Mars, and both missions were declared a success.

The Case of the Ice Village Vandal

(page 29)

Who stole the elf's circuit board?
• **Mr Kroft.** The lights from the sign were keeping him awake at night, so he sneaked into the elf and stole the circuit board.

How did Max and Alison solve the case?
• Max saw Mr Kroft use keys to sneak into the clubhouse. That reminded Max that Lindsey had said Zack was always losing his keys. When Mr Kroft cut Zack a new pair of keys, he cut a set for himself so he could sneak into the elf.
• The note Mr Dumont found demanded that the sign be turned off at night. Only Mr Kroft was bothered by the lights at night. Everyone else complained about the noise of the moving arm.
• When the note was left in the golf clubhouse, Zack and Becca were in the woods and Lindsey was at home. Only Mr Kroft was around to plant the note.
• Zack was showing Becca some owl pellets he found in the woods. It proved that the snowy owl was living on the golf course.
Conclusion
Mr Kroft admitted to stealing the circuit board and returned it to Mr Dumont. When shown the snowy owl pellets, Mr Dumont agreed to turn off the elf's moving arm so the birds wouldn't be scared. He also turned off the sign after the Ice Village closed for the night. That way Mr Kroft could get some sleep.

The Case of the Cast–off Costume

(page 35)

Who smashed the grouch costume?
• **Basher McGintley.** Although Basher enjoyed being in the Christmas show, he was embarrassed by his grouch costume. He thought that if he damaged the costume he would be allowed to wear his jeans on stage.

How did Basher do it?
• After Saturday's rehearsal, Basher wedged Jeff Coleman's grouch gang hat in the fire exit door. After everyone left, Basher sneaked back and took the costume to the tobogganing hill and ruined it.

How did Max solve the case?
• Courtney mentioned that Basher didn't like the costume. And Mrs Janssen said Basher had asked to wear his jeans on stage instead.

Case Solutions

• Only Basher and Jessica wore red wool hats. But Jessica's mittens and hat were made of expensive angora, so they didn't match the fibres Zoe found on the grouch's head. That left only Basher's old red wool hat.

• Max and Alison spied Basher trying to get rid of the grouch's henchman hat. The bully was surprised when Dwayne and Shayne arrived and had to drop it in the snow.

Conclusion

After seeing that the wool fibres matched his red hat, Basher admitted to ruining the grouch costume. He said he covered his cold hands with his red hat when he punched the grouch's papier-mâché head.

Basher was sorry and still wanted to be in the play. Courtney repaired the costume as well as she could and Basher went on stage. He acted like a movie star and the audience gave him a standing ovation.

The Case of the Slime Tank Sabotage

(page 41)

Who sabotaged the slime tank?

• **Johnny Vile.** Johnny was sick of taking apart the *Punk My Bike* set every week. He sabotaged the slime tank so the quiz show would be cancelled.

How did Max solve the case?

• After the accident, Johnny told Mrs Finder that he had just arrived at the TV station. But Johnny told Max and Alison that he'd been at the TV station working on the set all morning. Plus, the security guard spotted him at the slime tank early in the morning.

• Johnny knew about the bolts being cut, but Max and Alison hadn't told anyone about the bolts yet.

• There were tools, including a hacksaw, lying around the set of *Punk My Bike*. Johnny used them to cut off the bolt tops.

• Basher found the bolt tops beside the tank. He took them but didn't tell anyone.

Conclusion

Johnny admitted to cutting the bolts. Bull O'Wiley agreed not to cancel the quiz show. The footage of the slime tank bursting was shown on TV around the world and made the quiz show an instant hit with viewers.

Case Solutions

The Case of the Lost Lobster

(page 49)

Who stole Twiggy the lobster?
• **Katlyn.** She thought it was cruel to put the lobster on display. She tried to make it look like Twiggy escaped so Lilly wouldn't keep him in the tank anymore. But Katlyn fell off the stool when scooping Twiggy out of the tank and broke the restaurant window. She panicked. She couldn't afford to replace the window, so she asked Patricio to hide Twiggy in the cellar of the cinema overnight. Then, Patricio snapped the lock on Judy's shop so they could hide Twiggy inside and put the blame on her.

How did Alison solve the case?
• Alison spotted Katyln's pink bracelet in Twiggy's tank.
• Lilly was afraid Twiggy would pinch her, so she probably wouldn't pick him up.
• Katlyn said Lilly was the only person with keys to the restaurant, but Katlyn told Patricio she had to lock up the restaurant.
• When Katlyn arrived for their picnic, Patricio said, "We haven't been waiting long." He had Twiggy in the cooler.

• Alison's uncle's cooler smelled of fish the next day because Patricio had used it to carry Twiggy.
• When they found Twiggy in Judy's shop, the lock on the shop was broken. If Judy had put the lobster there, she wouldn't have broken the lock.

Conclusion
Katlyn admitted to taking the lobster and Patricio confessed to helping her. Katlyn didn't lose her job, but her wages went to paying for the broken window. Lilly agreed to donate Twiggy to a nearby ocean research centre, where he now lives free from window-banging tourists.

How? Why? Where?

The Case of the Movie Set Mischief

(page 57)

Who is trying to hurt Jasmin?
• **Miranda Madison.** She was angry that she didn't get the role as Dogtown Malone's sidekick. Since they had just started filming the movie, Miranda figured she would get the leading role if Jasmin was hurt.

How did Max solve the case?
• Rex gave Jasmin her lunch, but he got it from Miranda. She had lots of time to put the old tuna into the sandwiches.
• Rex said the ninja who moved the sandbags before the light fell was "skinny." That means it couldn't have been Leonard.
• The ninja who leaped from the bushes was wearing a red bandana — it was Miranda.

Conclusion
Miranda was found hiding in her hotel room. She admitted she'd tried to hurt Jasmin and was fired from the movie. That night, she slipped out of the hotel and hasn't been seen in the movie business since. Alison eagerly took the job as Jasmin's stunt double.

The Case of the Hijacked Hat

(page 63)

Who stole Dogtown Malone's hat?
• **Leonard.** The celebrity photographer was under so much pressure to deliver another scandal for his magazine that he tried to make one by taking Ridge Thorton's lucky hat.

How did Alison solve the case?
• In his cleaner's uniform, Leonard had access to the luggage unloading area, where he could take Ridge Thorton's hat out of the box.
• There was a mysterious brown shape in Leonard's cleaning trolley.
• When Leonard was leaving the airport he said he was finished being a cleaner, but he was still carrying a rubbish bag. Dogtown's hat was inside the bag.

Conclusion
Airport security caught up with Leonard before he could get away with Dogtown's hat. The celebrity photographer admitted to stealing the hat while the luggage was being unloaded from the aeroplane. Ridge Thorton got his hat back and the movie was finished on time.

The Case of the Screaming Screening

(page 69)

Who stole Jasmin's necklace?
• **Ashton Cruz.** He needed money to pay for acting lessons, so he snipped off the expensive necklace while he was fixing Jasmin's hair in the women's toilets.

How did Alison solve the case?
• The scissors found in the cinema were haircutting scissors. Ashton told Max he went to hairdressing school.
• Alison found the necklace clasp in the women's toilets, so she knew that's where the robbery took place.
• Jasmin's necklace was missing before she went in to take her seat in the cinema, but she didn't notice until the lights went out.
• Petra was on stage when the jewels were taken, so it couldn't have been her.
• Anabella Jockey was in the lobby while Ashton and Jasmin were in the toilet, so she couldn't have been the thief.

Conclusion
The police found the necklace in Ashton's pocket and took him away. Everyone returned to their seats to watch *Dogtown Malone III*. It was a huge hit. The audience gave the whole cast, including Max and Alison, a standing ovation.

Ghoulish Gravestones
(page 22)

1. M.T. Toomb (Empty tomb)
2. Dr. Acula (Dracula)
3. Ricky D. Bones (Rickety bones)
4. R.U. Next (Are you next?)
5. Izzy Dead (Is he dead?)
6. Dee Parted (Departed)
7. Frank N. Stein (Frankenstein)
8. Ima Ghost (I'm a ghost)
9. Rustin Peace (Rest in peace)

Keyboard Code
(page 28)

Message:
Team Discovery:
You landed on Mars!
Way to go!
Commander Ripley

Places, Everyone
(page 34)

Alison was goalie. Ethan played left defence and Max played right defence. Jessica played centre, with Basher on left wing and Becca on right wing.

What Kind of Detective Would You Be?
(page 40)

Ratings:

Mostly As: Top-notch private eye. From finding clues to getting the facts from witnesses, you'd crack the case wide open.

Mostly Bs: Forensics specialist. You pay attention to the smallest details and work well with a team.

Mostly Cs: Armchair detective. Solving mysteries may be cool, but it's even cooler to watch someone on a TV show solve a crime.

Slime Time
(page 48)

Don't Forget to Bring:
- notebook
- tweezers
- clear tape
- plastic bags
- camera
- measuring tape
- magnifying glass

Stick With It (page 56)

Stamps © Canada Post Corporation (2007). Reproduced with Permission.

1. The three identical stamps are:

2. The stamp that is upside down and backwards is:

3. The stamp from New Zealand is:

4. The stamp with a lighthouse on it is:

5. The stamp worth 26 pence is:

6. The stamps featuring birds are:

Chain Reaction (page 68)

The common things are:

1. ticket
2. screen
3. keys
4. can be opened
5. arrive by delivery
6. round
7. string
8. fly

Photos: (p. 68): travelpixpro/iStockphoto (theater); Redbaron/Dreamstime (laptop); xyno/iStockphoto (door); haveseen/iStockphoto (envelope); khz/iStockphoto (pizza); webking/iStockphoto (yo-yo); mashabuba/iStockphoto (kite); Kickers/iStockphoto (plane).

On the Red Carpet (page 74)

- Tad has **10** bodyguards
- Petra has **5**
- Anabella has **4**
- Ridge and Jasmin have **3**
- Ashton has **1**

How to Make Your Own Comic

Did you know anyone can write comics? Liam O'Donnell here, **Max Finder Mystery** creator. From superhero action adventures to puzzling mysteries, you can tell any story with comics. And I'm going to show you how to write one.

CATCHING IDEAS
Every comic starts with an idea and it can land in your brain at any time. I carry a notebook that fits in my jacket pocket so I'm always ready to catch an idea.

Sometimes a writer's brain is empty of ideas. When this happens, I ask myself: "What if...?" Then I put something that doesn't happen every day after the "if" to give me a story idea.

Max Finder Mystery Ideas

What if...

- Basher hired Max to solve a crime?

- Max and Alison solved a mystery at the zoo – an escaped koala?

- Alison was accused of a crime and Max had to prove she was innocent?

Setting the Scene

The setting is the place and time your story happens. Be specific when you create your setting. If your story takes place in a house, describe the house. A house in the city, a spooky mansion on a hill, and a cottage by the sea are all houses, but each could tell a different story.

Being specific not only creates a better story for your readers, it also tells your illustrator what to draw. But don't hog all the creativity! Let the illustrator add his or her ideas and you'll have an even better comic.

Creating Characters

Make your characters unique by avoiding stereotypes, those overly simple characters you've seen before. The pimply-faced computer nerd who gets bullied is an example of a stereotype. A good way to avoid stereotypes is to give your characters an unexpected interest that doesn't fit the stereotype. Basher McGintley is a grouchy bully, but he also loves acting in school plays.

Jake Granger – Tall, 12-year-old with action-hero good looks. He like magic and thinks he is psychic. He also plays sports and loves being outside. He wears skater-style clothes – semi-baggy jeans, cool T-shirts and chunky skater shoes.

Writers create character sketches for illustrators to use when they're drawing. In a few sentences, describe what your characters look like, how old they are, what they like wearing, and anything else that makes them unique. Here's a character sketch of Jake Granger.

Building the Plot

Your characters need something to do, so it's time to create your plot. The best plots involve a problem your character must solve. Think of your characters as riding a bike up a hill. Use your imagination and follow these steps:

2. Building

Block your character's goal. Jake Granger investigates the crimes, and no one will talk to Max about the case.

3. Conclusion

Have your character overcome the problem. Max looks for clues until he learns Jake's secret.

1. Intro

Give your character a goal. In **The Case of the Back-to-School Sneak** (page 11), Max wants to catch the thief.

Writing the Script

Now you're ready to start writing your comic script. A comic script is part story and part illustration manual telling the illustrator what to draw. Here's what a Max Finder Mystery script looks like:

Put the author's name, comic title, draft number, and date at the top of every page.

Comic page number shows which comic page you're working on.

The **Scene Description** tells the illustrator what to draw.

The panel number shows which panel or box you're working on.

Caption boxes set the scene for the reader.

10/04

O'Donnell, Liam   Max Finder Mystery

The Case of the Back-to-School Sneak: Draft 2

Page 1   Panel 1

Exterior Central Meadows playground, morning kids are playing football in the playground. Alison holds a football. In the playground is Ethan Webster. He looks upset. Max crouches beside Ethan and has picked up Ethan's coat. The pockets are empty and Ethan's video-game player is missing.

CAPTION

Did you know the Egyptian pharaohs enjoyed the first magic show over 6,500 years ago? Max Finder here, fact collector and ace detective. It's a new school year and that means new kids, new teachers and already a new mystery.

ETHAN

Max, somebody took my video-game player from my coat pocket!

MAX

None of the other coats were touched. The thief knew where to look.

1.

You're ready to hand your script to the illustrator.

Dialogue is what your characters say. Add the character's name to show who is talking. Keep dialogue short to fit the speech bubble.

Script page number refers to the pages in your comic script. There are usually more script pages than comic pages.

Liam O'Donnell

Liam O'Donnell is the author of many children's books and the creator of *Max Finder Mystery* and the *Graphic Guide Adventures* series of graphic novels. In addition to writing for kids, Liam is a teacher, plays video games and goes camping (but not all at the same time). He lives in Toronto, Canada. You can visit him online at: **www.liamodonnell.com**.